Mario Duschenes

METHOD
for the
RECORDER

For group work, individual teaching, or self instruction

PART ONE

SOPRANO (DESCANT) AND TENOR

AMP 7107
ISBN 0-7935-7855-8

Berandol Music Limited / SCARBOROUGH, ONTARIO

SOLE SELLING AGENTS

Associated Music Publishers, Inc.

DISTRIBUTED BY

HAL•LEONARD®
CORPORATION
7777 W. BLUEMOUND RD. P.O. BOX 13819 MILWAUKEE, WI 53213

FINGERING CHART
for all five recorders

Baroque *(or English)* and German fingering

Soprano
Tenor

Sopranino
Alto

Bass

GERMAN FINGERING IN SQUARES.

When more than one fingering is given for
the same note, the first shown is the one most
commonly used on Baroque Recorders.

4

INTRODUCTION

The recorder (French: flûte-à-bec, German: Blockflöte, Italian: flauto dolce) is a wood-wind instrument belonging to the flute family. Flute-type instruments are believed to be among the most ancient, various kinds having existed in China, India and Egypt long before the Greek civilization.

For many centuries the recorder was the most popular member of the flute family, and it is often referred to by Milton, Shakespeare and Pepys, among others. The name "recorder" is derived from a long obsolete verb "to record", which meant apparently "to warble" or sing like a bird. It is also sometimes called, "English flute" or "Fipple flute". The latter term refers to that part of the mouthpiece which differentiates the tone production of the recorder from that of the side blown or transverse flute. Wind instruments produce their tone by the vibration of an air column in the tube. To produce a tone on an instrument of the flute family, the air column has to be split by a sharp edge (no reeds are used). On the transverse flute, the air column is directed against this edge by the player's lips, and good tone depends on his ability to do this correctly. On the recorder however, the fipple provides a narrow air channel in the mouthpiece and guides the air in the required direction. Because of this air channel (or "windway") it is relatively easy to produce a tone on the recorder.

The pitch of a note depends on the number of vibrations in the tube. The shorter the column of air, the faster the vibrations and the higher the note. The recorder has seven holes in the front and one in the back. Some recorders have double holes for the two lowest semitones (see fingering chart). When all the holes are covered the instrument produces its lowest note, as the column of air in the tube is then at its longest. On bass recorders the bottom hole cannot be reached by the little finger of the right hand; therefore a metal key is provided to cover this hole. Some alto and tenor recorders are also equipped with such keys.

Michael Praetorius (1571-1621), the German composer and musicologist describes as many as eight recorders of different sizes. To-day five are commonly used:

	LOWEST NOTE	INTERVAL	
Sopranino	f''		about 9" long
	------	fourth	
Soprano or Descant	c''		
	------	fifth	
Alto or Treble	f'		
	------	fourth	
Tenor	c'		
	------	fifth	
Bass	f		about 3' long

Thus a group of recorders resembles a mixed choir in that the range and the relationship of registers are similar.

Recorders are not transposing instruments (as, for instance, Bb clarinet or F horn), but one can say that the fundamental scale of the sopranino, alto and bass recorders is the F major scale; of soprano and tenor, the C major scale. The bass has a chromatic range of roughly one and a half octaves; the other recorders have two octaves. The skilful alto player can produce even more than two octaves.

To facilitate reading, music for the Sopranino, Soprano and Bass recorders is written an octave lower than the actual sound.

Works Written For The Recorder

Essentially a folk instrument in ancient times, the recorder first began to attract the attention of composers during the sixteenth century. Amongst the works of the next centuries we find a great deal written specifically for the recorder. Besides this, however, there is much instrumental music which does not specify the instruments to be used, but leaves the choice to the discretion of the performer. (e.g., Loeillet's "Sonate pour flûte-à-bec ou hautbois ou violon ou viole de gambe avec basse continue", or Palestrina's "Ricercari a quatro con ogni sorte de stromenti", - "any kind of instruments"). A glance at the catalogue of any leading music publisher will convince the reader of the wealth of recorder music available.

J. S. Bach used the recorder ("flauto") in a dozen or more of his cantatas and in the Brandenburg Concerti, No. 2 and No. 4. (It is largely because of the lack of competent recorder players that flutes are usually substituted in performances of these works). After 1750 the recorder fell into disuse and was not revived until 1925. Since that time contemporary composers have also contributed to the literature of the instrument.

The recorder can be played alone or in combination with other recorders or other instruments. There are publications for any number of recorders from solo to octet. Probably the quartet (soprano, alto, tenor and bass) is the most satisfying of all recorder combinations. A solo recorder sounds charming with percussion accompaniment, especially in dances of the fourteenth and fifteenth centuries. The possibilities of combining recorders with other instruments are too numerous to list. There is a great deal of music for one or more recorders with piano or harpischord accompaniment. Another excellent combination is alto recorder, violin or oboe or flute, and keyboard instrument. There are also endless possibilities for accompanying the voice.

When buying music it is helpful to be familiar with a few expressions used by English and German publishers. As a rule, English publishers call the soprano a "descant recorder" and the alto a "treble recorder". In German the soprano and tenor are often called C - Flöte or C - Blockflöte, the alto, F - Flöte or F - Blockflöte.

The German "für zwei Blockflöten im Quintabstand" means "for two recorders a fifth apart" such as soprano and alto.

Figured bass, basso continuo (or simply continuo), Generalbass, or Bezifferter Bass means a part for a keyboard instrument with 'cello or viola da gamba ad libitum.

How To Choose a Recorder

As a beginner, you should take up either the soprano or the alto, leaving the other recorders for later. If your hands are particularly small, start with the soprano. Otherwise the choice of your instrument should be guided by the music you want to play. The soprano is more suitable for playing folk songs or for leading a group of players, the alto for sonatas, concerti and chamber music. The alto is usually more expensive than the soprano. Buy the best recorder you can afford, it pays in the long run.

Care Of The Instrument

Before starting to play, it is advisable to warm the mouthpiece by holding it in one's hand for a few minutes. This improves the tone and reduces condensation in the air channel. The channel and mouthpiece should be kept as dry as possible at all times. A new recorder should not be played more than fifteen minutes at a time, in order to accustom the wood to the moisture. The inside of a recorder should always be dried with a swab or cloth after playing. If the tone becomes hoarse, place a finger on the "window" and blow sharply through the mouthpiece, thus clearing away moisture or any other obstruction in the channel. The edge in the "window" under the mouthpiece should not be touched since damage to this part of the recorder will spoil its tone.

Tuning

If the overall pitch of an instrument tends to be sharp, it can sometimes be corrected by pulling out the head-joint slightly. When doing this, always use a screwing motion.

Fingering

Manufacturers make recorders with either "German" or "Baroque" (sometimes called "English") fingering. The student should know which type he has in order to learn the correct fingering for his instrument. In this book both types of fingering are given. A glance at the chart will show that only a few fingerings differ in the two systems. The Baroque system is the original one and results in better intonation, but the German system (invented around 1930) is advisable for small children since the fingering technique is simpler in the keys of C and F.

The fingering chart shows how each note is played:
● - closed hole   O - open hole   ◖ - 1/2 or 3/4 closed (thumb).

The chart gives those fingerings which are most commonly used. This does not ensure perfect intonation on every recorder. Should a note not sound perfectly on pitch if fingered according to the chart, the student should experiment and find his own fingering for that particular note.

Picture No. 3 shows you how to hold the instrument in a correct, relaxed position. The

1

2

3

4

5

6

thumb of the left hand covers the hole at the back. The three top holes are covered by the index, middle, and ring finger of the same hand. The thumb of the right hand supports the recorder from underneath and should be placed behind the fourth and fifth holes from the top. The four fingers of the right hand cover the remaining holes. Since you will not have to cover any holes with the right hand while studying the first few pages of this book, use the fingers of your right hand to hold the recorder. Keep them next to the holes in order to get them used to their positions for the future (Picture No. 4).

In the beginning, one of your main difficulties will be covering the holes completely. Impure notes are caused by the leakage of air through holes which are improperly closed. Therefore be sure to keep your fingers flat on the recorder as shown on picture No. 3. Cover the holes with the pads of your fingers, not with the finger tips. There is no need to use pressure; simply make sure that you are covering the holes completely. Pressure will only result in cramping the hands. When using a relaxed technique, you will be able to play the recorder without tiring.

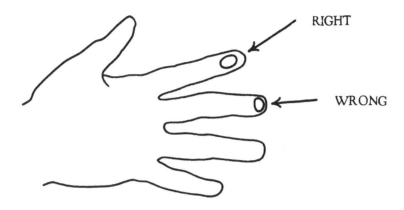

Blowing

Picture No. 1 shows a recorder player with good posture. If possible, use a music stand while playing. Pinch your lips very slightly and place the mouthpiece between them in such a way that the mouthpiece remains dry. Breathe deeply from the diaphragm; do not raise your shoulders. Keep in mind that in France and Switzerland the recorder is called "flûte douce" ("soft flute"). Blow gently, but hard enough to produce a warm tone; blow evenly to produce a steady tone. Sustained blowing will avoid the rise and fall of the pitch of a note. You will find that low notes require a little less air. Since a musical phrase does not often permit a lot of time for breathing in, practise taking a deep breath quickly. Breathe naturally as you would when reading aloud. Breathe when the musical phrase demands it, whether you really need the air or not.

Always try to play perfectly in tune. This should be your highest aim and depends mainly on your breath control and the use of correct fingering. Blowing hard raises the pitch, blowing softly lowers it.

Tonguing

Unless you slur (see "phrasing"), start each note with the syllable "du" or "tu". This procedure, used on all wind instruments, is called "tonguing". It means that, immediately preceding a note, you place your tongue above your teeth against the palate - neither touching the teeth nor the mouthpiece of the recorder and then release the tongue just as you do when you pronounce the letter "d" or "t" Use the "du" technique (soft tonguing) for cantabile playing and the harder "tu" for gayer passages.

Phrasing

Legato is indicated by slurs (⌒) between notes of different pitch. Legato is played by "tonguing" only the first of these slurred notes. The study of legato playing has been left out of this book because it involves a technique which is difficult for the beginner, and the author feels that the student advances more quickly and gets more enjoyment out of his studies if first of all he learns to play all the notes which the recorder can produce. Once this has been achieved, slurring may be practised. One should bear in mind, however, that certain intervals can only be slurred with difficulty. A very gentle tonguing ("recorder legato") produces almost as good a result for cantabile or smooth playing as the real legato. Try to achieve a maximum difference between staccato and legato (real legato or "recorder legato"). This is called "phrasing" and it will help to make your playing sound interesting. After all, the recorder cannot use "forte" and "piano" (loud and soft) to the same extent as other instruments.

MUSIC NOTATION, TERMS AND SYMBOLS

The following section does not pretend to be a complete course in musical theory. It is intended merely as a guide for those who have little or no musical experience.

Musical sounds are represented by "notes" whose pitch is indicated by their position on the "staff": the higher the pitch, the higher the position on the staff. The staff consists of five lines and four spaces which are numbered upwards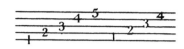

A note may be placed on one of the lines or in one of the spaces. When notes are required which are too high or too low to find a place on the staff, short lines are added. These short lines are called "leger lines".

Notes are named after the first seven letters of the alphabet - a, b, c, d, e, f, g. The position of these notes on the staff is determined by "clefs". The "g" or "treble clef" winds around the second line of the staff:

The note on this line is therefore called "g":

So we can easily identify all the other notes

Music for sopranino, soprano, alto and tenor recorders is written in the treble clef. The bass recorder uses the "f" or "bass clef": It is written on the fourth line and marks the position of the note "f": from which the position of the other notes may be ascertained.

The length of a note is indicated as follows:

o	=	whole note
♩	=	1/2 note (Two 1/2 notes = one whole note)
♩	=	1/4 note (Two 1/4 notes = one 1/2 note)
♪	=	1/8 note (Two 1/8 notes = one 1/4 note)
♪	=	1/16 note (Two 1/16 notes = one 1/8 note)

In other words, one whole note (o) equals two half notes (♩), or four quarter notes (♩), or eight eighth notes (♪), or sixteen sixteenth notes (♪).

Two or more notes are sometimes connected by a heavy line or lines:

eighth notes   sixteenth notes

AMP-7107

⅜, 4/4, 6/8 etc. At the beginning of every piece of music you will find a "time signature" in the form of a fraction. The upper figure indicates the number of beats (or counts) to a "measure", while the lower figure indicates what kind of note has the value of one beat. For example:

4/4 means four beats to the measure with each quarter note (or its equivalent) to be counted as one beat.

6/8 means six beats to the measure with each eighth note (or its equivalent) to be counted as one beat.

4/4 is also known as "common" time and may be written. **C**

A "measure" is the space between two "vertical" lines on the staff, known as "bar lines". The end of each section of a piece is marked by a "double bar".

"Flats" and "sharps" are used to change the pitch of a note by a half-tone or "semitone". The raising of a note by a semitone is indicated by placing a sharp (♯) before the note. The lowering of a note by a semi-tone is indicated by placing a flat (♭) before the note.

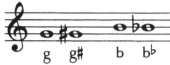

A flat or sharp written as part of the "key signature" at the beginning of a line, immediately following the clef sign, must be observed for the entire line, unless cancelled by the "natural" sign (♮)

When a flat or sharp not listed in the key signature appears during the course of a piece, it is called an "accidental" and is effective for one bar only:

Repeat from the beginning

Repeat everything between the two sets of dots

If the endings of a repeated section are different they are marked as follows:

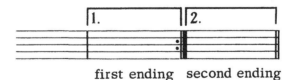

first ending   second ending

Play the first ending, the first time only. On the repeat, omit the first ending and go to the second ending.

⌢ This is a "pause" sign or "fermata" which tells you to prolong the note or rest over which it is written. It is also used to designate the end ("fine") of a piece.

D.C. or Da Capo: go back to the beginning.
Da capo al fine: go back to the beginning and continue to the word "fine"
Fine: conclusion.

AMP-7107

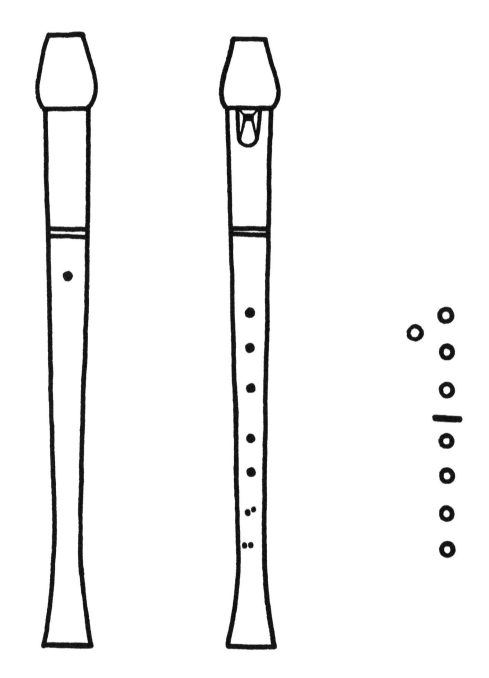

AMP-7107

A dot following a note increases the value of that note by half.

Good finger coordination is required to move smoothly from B to C and from C to B. See that the opening of one hole coincides exactly with the closing of the other.

When playing this note, remove your thumb from the recorder, do not use it as a support. See picture Nº6

+F♯ is written to indicate that this and more of the following numbers are in the key of G major although the actual F♯ does not occur in the piece.

Mary Had a Little Lamb

Fais Dodo

The Little Bridge

Eighth notes

Eighth notes are twice as fast as quarter notes. Play two eighth notes on one beat.

Two notes of the same pitch connected with a tie (⌒) are played as one note.

The same exercise could be written this way:

The rhythm ♩. ♪ has to be practised a great deal since it presents some difficulty.

To facilitate the understanding of the dotted rhythm, let us count the beats in a different way: give each note twice as many beats as in the past.

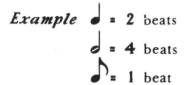

Example ♩ = **2** beats

♩ = **4** beats

♪ = **1** beat

Count **8** beats to the bar

Count **6** beats to the bar

Similarly if you count ♪ as 1 beat, ♩. will be counted as **3** beats.

Count **8** beats to the bar

When you can do this easily, count "one and two and three and four and" instead of "one, two, three, four, five, six, seven, eight".

1 and 2 and 3 and 4 and   1 and 2 and 3 and 4 and

After some practice you can drop the "and" and play counting "one, two, three, four"

1   2   3   4   1   2   3   4

Make sure you place your ♪ between counts 2 & 3 and 4 & 1

Count **4** beats to the bar

Theme from a Piano Sonata by Mozart

THE RESTS

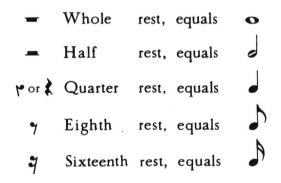

		rest, equals	
▬	Whole	rest, equals	𝅝
▬	Half	rest, equals	𝅗𝅥
𝄽 or ↯	Quarter	rest, equals	♩
↱	Eighth	rest, equals	♪
↱	Sixteenth	rest, equals	𝅘𝅥𝅯

1 2 3 4   1 2 3 4

1 2 3 4   1   2   3   4

May Song

Jingle Bells

Let us stop for a minute and consider whether you are observing the following important rules as outlined in the introduction:

Are you "tonguing" every note?

Are you using the correct fingering?

Are you observing the correct rhythm of notes and rests?

Are all fingers ready in playing position ($\frac{1}{2}$ inch above the hole) so that you are able to play all pieces without hesitating before certain notes? See picture No. 4

Are you keeping your fingers flat and are you using the pads of the fingers, not the tips, to close the holes?

Are your fingers, hands, arms relaxed?

Are you keeping the mouthpiece dry?

Are you playing in tune and is your tone even?

Re-read the chapter on breathing.

Play slowly enough to keep an even speed throughout the piece; one is always tempted to play easy passages faster.

Go Tell Aunt Rhody

The Bee

Dance

M. Praetorius

J'ai du Bon Tabac

Cuckoo

The Three Farmers

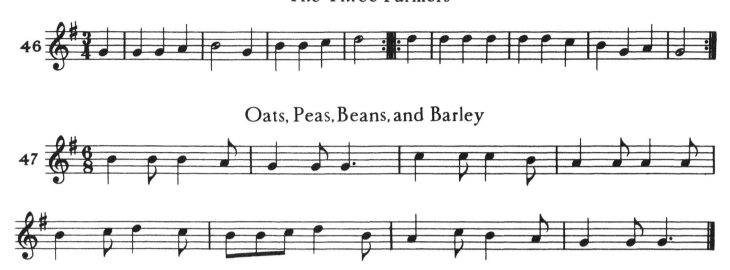

Oats, Peas, Beans, and Barley

HINTS ON PRACTISING

There are many ways of obtaining good results in practising, and every student will develop his own system. Here is one suggestion for overcoming difficulties in finger technique. It seldom happens that <u>all</u> the notes of a melody are of equal difficulty; therefore, in learning a piece one should concentrate on the difficult passages rather than play the whole over and over again. Suppose one passage of six notes in a piece gives you trouble. A good method of overcoming the difficulty is to concentrate on these six notes in the following manner: Practise the 3rd and 4th notes of the passage over and over again until you have mastered them. Then play notes 3, 4 & 5 as follows; 3-4-5-4-3-4-5-4 etc. Then add the second note and play; 2-3-4-5-4-3-2-3-4-5 and so on, until you can play the entire passage fluently.

Quand J'etais Chez Mon Père

The Nightingale

AMP-7107

Winter Good-bye

The "Ten Easy Duets" at the end of this book can now be studied.

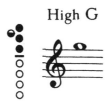

High G

As the picture shows, the thumb hole is about ¾ closed. The thumb should be bent and the nail used to close the hole in such a way that only a small portion remains open. Using the nail rather than the fleshy part of the thumb gives one far more control over the size of the opening. The clarity of high notes depends on the observance of this important rule. This procedure is used for all notes above and including high E. Should you have difficulty in producing high notes clearly, change the position of the thumb slightly to make a larger or smaller opening. (As a rule the opening should be smallest for very high notes). See picture Nº 5.

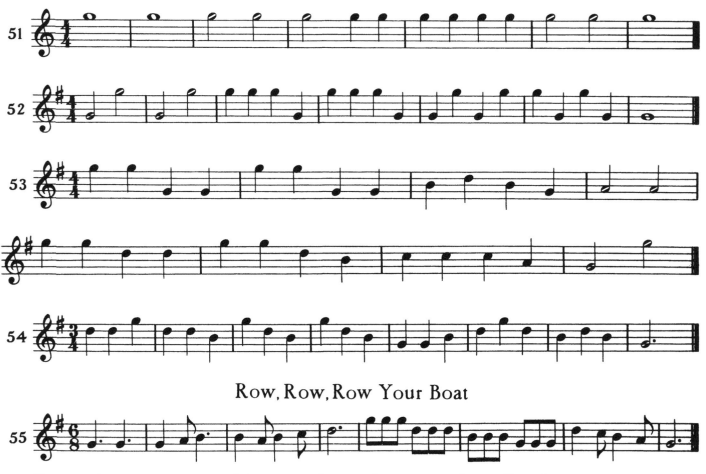

Row, Row, Row Your Boat

Practise this piece counting 6 beats to a bar until you can play it fluently.

Then count 2 beats of ♪♪♪ each.

AMP-7107

Oh, Dear, What Can the Matter Be

Emphasize the character of a piece by varying the tonguing.
Gay tunes call for a harder tonguing (tu), calm ones for a softer tonguing (du).

High A

Should you have any difficulty in playing this note, blow a little harder
and change the thumb position.

High E

Use the fingering with <u>open</u> thumb-hole only when E is the highest note of a passage.

While playing G or A, keep the fingers of your right hand ready to play E without hesitation.

Au Clair de la Lune

D. C.

Twinkle, Twinkle Little Star

The Muffin Man

72

Les Petites Marionettes

73

The Farmer in the Dell

74

Hush, My Babe

75

D.C.

Perrine Était Servante

76

24

Oh! Susanna

77

La Belle Françoise

78

Il Était une Bergère

79

En Roulant Ma Boule

80

25

AMP-7107

My Bonnie

V'la l'Bon Vent

slower   *D. C.*

Marie Madeleine

Low **D**

This note has to be played gently and the holes must be closed most carefully

Ah! Si Mon Moine Voulait Danser!

A La Claire Fontaine

Theme from Beethoven's Symphony Nº IX

Bonsoir, Mes Amis, Bonsoir

Fine

D. C.

Did You Ever See a Lassie

Au Fond Des Campagnes

Hot Cross Buns

Low C This note presents some difficulty to the beginner. Do not use pressure in covering the holes, but be very careful to close them completely. The slightest leakage of air will spoil the note. Until you can produce the note easily, blow very softly. If after a few attempts you do not get the desired note, do not persist in your attempts as your hands might become cramped. Go on practising other notes and leave low C for the next day. The right hand will eventually get used to the position and C will be obtained quite easily.

If your recorder has a movable foot-joint, turn it to a convenient position for the little finger of the right hand.

Mary Had a Little Lamb

Low F

Baroque   German

(see foreword)

May Song

122

Wie Schoen Leuchtet Der Morgenstern (Chorale)

123

Auld Lang Syne

124

Dixie

125

What Shall We Do With a Drunken Sailor

126

Scale of C major

C major arpeggio

High F

Baroque   German

If you have a recorder with baroque fingering note the difference between low F and high F.
Low F is played with the little finger of the right hand, high F without.

Oats, Peas, Beans, and Barley

She'll Be Comin' Round the Mountain

Vive la Compagnie

Yankee Doodle

Isabeau s'y Promène

A-Hunting We Will Go

The Lincolnshire Poacher

La Volta
W. Byrd

Dance by Claude Gervaise

God Save The Queen

151

Au Clair de la Lune

152

Little Boy Blue

153

Gai Lon La, Gai le Rosier

154

Polly Put the Kettle On

155

Dance

V. Hausmann

156

C'est L'Aviron

157

The Mulberry Bush

Il Était un Petit Navire

O! No John

Mariann' S'en Va-t-au Moulin

Polly-Wolly-Doodle

Youpe! Youpe! sur la Rivière

Home on the Range

Margoton

High F#

John Peel

Scale of G major

Bb, A#

Scale of F major

A Capital Ship

En Passant par la Lorraine

Baa, Baa, Black Sheep

Vive la Canadienne

Sumer Is Icumen In

Lavender's Blue

Lovely Evening (Round)

Sing a Song of Sixpence

London Bridge

Malbrough S'en Va-t-en Guerre

D. C.

C# Db

Prayer of Thanksgiving

Bourrée by Johann Krieger

(A# same fingering as B♭)

Christus, Der Uns Selig Macht (Chorale)

Chorales should be played "molto cantabile" (very smoothly)

AMP-7107

Gavotte

J. S. Bach

190

G#, Ab

191

192

193

The Jolly Miller

194

I've Been Workin' on the Railroad

195

Old King Cole

196

Bobby Shaftoe

Dance by Claude Gervaise

High Bb, A#

F major scale

Bb major arpeggio

G minor arpeggio

Are you observing the key signature for every piece? Make it a rule to look at the key and time signature before playing. Are you adapting your "tonguing" to the character of the music (slow, solemn, lyrical pieces should be tongued smoothly; gay, fast pieces should be played more staccato with robust tonguing).

High B

This note and the next two higher ones are difficult to play. Only good quality recorders will produce a pleasant tone in this register. The thumb should be tried in various positions and the air forced slightly until the sound is satisfactory. Most recorders produce a better tone in this register when the thumb hole is 80 to 90% closed.

AMP-7107

B minor scale
206

B minor arpeggio
207

E minor arpeggio
208

G major arpeggio
209

D'Ou Viens-Tu, Bergère
210

High C
211

C major scale
212

C major arpeggio
213

Three Blind Mice
214

A minor arpeggio
215

F major arpeggio
216

Il Etait un Petit Navire

Eb, D#

Down in the Valley

Christ Lay in the Bonds of Death
(Chorale)

High G#, Ab

C minor scale

225

A minor scale

226

F minor scale

227

Chromatic scale

228

⁺Can only be played on recorders with double holes (see fingering chart)

Trills

Trills are written as follows:

This means that you alternate the written note with the next higher one in rapid succession. The key signature must of course be observed; example:

Alternate A and B flat

The rhythm of the trilled note must also be observed. When playing a trill, beginners tend to prolong a note beyond its given value and so disrupt the rhythm of the piece.

A recorder player must realize that on a number of notes trills cannot be executed although we may often find trill signs on such notes in printed music. Some recorder methods give a trill fingering for each note; however, since some of these fingerings produce notes which are very much out of tune, the following chart⁺only lists those trills that can be played reasonably in tune on a standard recorder. If the suggested fingerings do not give you a satisfactory result, try to find your own trill fingering by experimenting on your instrument.

*See Chart on page 48.

The importance of playing ▮▮▮▮, making up songs and pieces, and improvising melodies cannot be over-emphasized. Furthermo▮▮ ▮▮no recorder players should learn to transpose one octave down, alto players one octave up. A playe▮ ▮▮o is able to transpose is an asset to any recorder group. A great deal of quartet music is published with ▮ne alto part written one octave below the actual sound.

TEN EASY DUETS
for Soprano and Alto Recorders
① Mary Had a Little Lamb

② The Little Bridge

③ May Song

⁺The Alto recorder plays F♯ like this ▮ or ▮

46

④ Dance by Praetorius

⑤ J'ai du Bon Tabac

⑥ Fais Dodo

Fine

D.C.
al Fine

AMP-7107

⑦ Theme from Mozart's Sonata in A

⑧ Go Tell Aunt Rhody

⑨ The Three Farmers

⑩ Oats, Peas, Beans, and Barley

TRILL FINGERING CHART
for all five recorders
Baroque *(or English)* and German fingering

Soprano
Tenor

Soprano
Alto

Bass

GERMAN FINGERING IN SQUARES.